Megan and the Money Tree

Megan and the Money Tree

Introducing Your Child to Money and Finance

Emma Kennedy
Illustrations by Yvonne Hennessy

KITE BOOKS

Published by Kite Books
an imprint of Blackhall Publishing
Lonsdale House
Avoca Avenue
Blackrock
Co. Dublin
Ireland

e-mail: info@blackhallpublishing.com
www.blackhallpublishing.com

ISBN: 978-1-84218-219-2

Printed in Ireland by Colorman Ltd.

To my sister Megan, for letting me borrow her name.

Emma Kennedy is personal finance correspondent with *The Sunday Business Post*. She has a degree in Economics and Finance from University College Dublin (UCD) and is a qualified financial advisor, after completing a professional diploma in Financial Advice at UCD. She also holds an MA in Journalism from Dublin City University.

Acknowledgements

Thanks to my family, friends and colleagues. And a special thanks to Yvonne for the illustrations and Elizabeth for making this book a reality.

Contents

Introduction

As the effects of a massive global financial crisis continue to unfold, people everywhere are beginning to realise just how much the economy affects their lives.

From the young couple who can't afford their mortgage repayments to the small business owner who can't access credit, everyone has been squeezed by the recession and the meltdown in the banking sector.

Now, more than ever, it is vital that everyone understands how the system works. However, every generation has its financial ups and downs, and a solid grasp of money matters is always relevant.

Financial literacy is a key life skill, but one that is largely overlooked by the educational system and the existing curriculum.

At primary level, children are introduced to money skills while learning maths. A number of basic financial concepts, including budgeting and money management, are touched on in subjects such as Maths, Business Studies and Home Economics at secondary school.

However, despite curriculum reviews, reports and recommendations, financial education remains something that slots into other subjects, rather than being taught as a stand-alone subject and given the emphasis it deserves.

It's not just up to schools to equip children with the financial skills they need for life. Parents have a role to play too. But some view money matters as something that children should be shielded from. However, it is possible to give children the basic message and get them thinking about the concepts, without exposing them to the full facts or worrying them.

Taking a gentle approach, it is possible to develop your child's money management skills and understanding of financial concepts, without making them worry about paying the bills each month.

Finance is not something to be afraid of. It doesn't have to be complicated. To explain basic financial ideas to your child, all you need to do is to make it easy, relevant and accessible. Strip out the jargon and pare it back to basic concepts. And start from there.

How to Use this Book

This book is designed to introduce children to basic financial concepts in an engaging manner, using language and ideas that make sense to younger readers.

Megan and the Money Tree is divided into two distinct sections and is designed to be used by both adults and children. Each section has six chapters. Each chapter

Introduction

in Part II contains questions and activities about the corresponding chapter in Part I (Megan's Story).

In Part I of the book – the children's part – we meet Megan, a little girl who learns about money when her family's income is wiped out unexpectedly.

Each of the chapters in Megan's story explores one central idea or key learning point, which can be used as a building block in your child's financial education. The six key learning points are as follows:

1. Unexpected things happen.
2. Events have consequences.
3. Risks don't always pay off.
4. Saving is gradual, with no quick fix.
5. Opportunity costs exist when you make a purchase.
6. Diversifying minimises risk.

Part II of the book is a resource for parents and teachers. It aims to get children thinking about Megan's story in terms of basic financial concepts. Each chapter helps your child to grasp the key learning point illustrated by the corresponding chapter in Megan's story. Once a child is thinking and talking about financial concepts, interactive exercises are used to explore the concepts in greater detail.

Part II of this book is designed as a springboard. It does not provide all the answers, but acts as a starting point.

Introduction

The six chapters in Part II are all structured in the same way, with three distinct sections – a summary, an explanation and suggested activities.

First, in the summary section, there's a quick recap of the content in the corresponding chapter in Part I of the book.

Then there are five questions for your child to consider, based on the material in the relevant chapter in Part I. Each question can be used to get your child to think about a financial idea and also provides an opportunity for you and your child to discuss a specific financial concept. Some of the questions are more subjective, and ask for your child's opinion. These questions are intended to get your child to really engage with the material and formulate his or her own views.

Next, in the explanation section, the chapter's key learning point is given a financial context and made relevant to the child by comparing it to day-to-day scenarios.

Finally, in the activities section, your child meets Megan again. She is on hand to help make learning fun with a range of carefully selected activities. First, she helps your child to develop their financial vocabulary by introducing a glossary of relevant financial terms for each chapter. Next, Megan sets a challenge for your child. These missions are designed to fit into a family's daily life and aim to develop your child's money skills in a practical way. There's also a game in each chapter, to allow your child to develop a deeper understanding of the new concepts he or she has just explored.

Introduction

What this Book Aims to Do

Megan and the Money Tree is designed to equip your child with a basic understanding of how money works. The simple story (Part I) and easy-to-follow guide (Part II) introduce a wide range of ideas and concepts, which will make finance more relevant to your child's own world.

However, this book also recognises that no two children are the same. Each child has their own interests and their own learning styles. So the activities in Part II of this book try to reflect the different ways that children learn. There are obstacle courses, painting activities and guessing games, all of which link to a financial concept. Some of these activities will suit creative children, some will suit active children and some will suit logical children. The activities are labelled "logic", "active" or "creative".

Megan and the Money Tree is based on the principle that teaching your child about money should not be a costly affair. The games and activities in Part II do not require parents or teachers to spend money on expensive toys. Instead, all the games can be played using things that are close to hand in a typical family home. Similarly, the missions that Megan asks younger readers to complete do not involve a cost for parents or teachers. The only resources required are time, patience and a healthy dollop of imagination.

1

Megan's Story

1

Crash

It all started with the storm – one of those nights when the wind howls and the rain pours down. Everything changed for me and my mum and dad that night.

Oh, by the way, I'm Megan. My dad grows apples. He sells them at the market in our town. I help him sometimes.

And, before that horrible storm, we used to have a huge, twisty apple tree in our garden.

Dad called it his money tree because he made money selling the apples from it. When I was little I thought all the leaves fluttering on the tree were €10 notes. Dad used to lift me up on his shoulders and I tried to pull off the leaves. I thought I was rich.

If only. Because every time I ask for a pony, my mum and dad say, "Money doesn't grow on trees." Which is exactly what they said when I wanted new runners, because everyone in my school got cool ones. Grown-ups always say that.

But I suppose my old runners come in handy sometimes. Like when I used to help my dad to gather up all the ripe apples to take to the market. Dad watered the apple tree a lot, so the ground was all squishy and muddy around it.

A while ago, Dad said it wasn't great weather for growing apples. It was very stormy and the apples were getting blown off the tree.

Dad and I were in the garden trying to pick the best apples and suddenly dark clouds filled the sky and it got really windy. Then we heard thunder – a sound like an angry bear growling.

We went into the house and I pressed my nose up against the window. The sky was dark. The apple tree looked like it was waving at me. Its branches blew up and down, and then from side to side, as the wind grew stronger and stronger.

That night I couldn't sleep. Neither could my cat Jake. He usually sleeps at the end of my bed, and that night he kept rolling about and meowing.

The wind was howling and the rain was falling in big drops. It sounded like someone was banging on my window. I put my head under the blankets, but I could still hear it.

Crash, creak, bang! I sat up in bed. I must have fallen asleep. But something had happened. Something loud enough to wake me up.

There was another crash, a loud groaning sound and a heavy bang. I slid out from under my blankets and kneeled up on my bed to look out the window. Jake jumped up on the bed beside me.

Outside in the garden, leaves danced in the wind. Lightning filled the sky and rain plopped to the ground. In the middle of it

all was the apple tree. But it wasn't tall and proud anymore. It wasn't even tall. It had fallen over, and its branches looked like broken bones.

I must have fallen back asleep because the next thing I remember it was Monday. And on Mondays my mum comes into my bedroom early to wake me up for school.

I hate mornings. I always scrunch up my eyes, snuggle down under the blankets and try to pretend it is still the middle of the night. But then Jake usually gets cranky and starts sulking, because he knows it is really the morning and he wants me to play with him. And Mum gets cranky too and tells me to hurry up or we'll all be late.

But this morning, the morning after the apple tree fell down, it was different.

Mum came into my bedroom looking tired. "Did you sleep okay, love? Did the storm wake you?" she asked me. So I told her about all the crashing and banging. She had heard it too.

After I put on my school uniform, I went downstairs for breakfast. Dad was sitting at the table, looking sad.

"I don't think we'll be selling any apples for a while," he said. "The tree is ruined after last night's storm."

2

Changes

So, remember how I told you that I used to help my dad with the apples, before the apple tree fell down? Well, this is what we did: we put all the apples into big baskets, we put the baskets into Dad's car and then we drove to the market.

If there were apples that were a bit bumpy and not quite good enough to sell, Mum made them into apple cake. And then Dad and I sold the apple cake at the market too.

Every Saturday we would stand at our stall at the market and sell the apples and the apple cake made from the bumpy apples. At the end of the day, we counted up all the money we had made.

After the tree fell down, there were no apples to sell and there was no money to count. My dad was worried. My mum was worried. They worried about not having enough money to buy food for us to eat. They worried about not having enough money to pay the man in the garage for petrol for the car. They just worried all the time.

When they were doing all this worrying, they pretended everything was fine. I hate

when grown-ups treat you like a baby and think you don't understand things. It's like when they tell you that taking a plaster off won't hurt. You know it will hurt and they know it will hurt, but they just say it won't, because they think it will make you feel better.

I missed how things were before the apple tree fell down. I used to like helping my dad to pick the apples and going to the market to sell them. Dad used to let me pick my favourite apple each week. I would take a big juicy bite and end up with a sticky chin from the apple juice.

And on Halloween we'd have toffee apples. I've always loved toffee apples. Well, until last Halloween, that is. That's when my tooth got stuck in an apple and my friends Aisling and Ciara kept laughing at me, and I got madder and madder.

Then my dad started laughing at me too, because the apple had my tooth in it and I was all gummy. I got really annoyed with him laughing at me in front of my friends and told him I didn't even like his stupid apples anyway.

But I suppose that wasn't really true. I did like the apples and I loved sitting in the garden under our apple tree. And Jake liked to sleep beside me in the shade. So I would sit and stroke him, listening to music.

And I used to get my pocket money on Saturdays, after we had finished counting up the money from selling the apples at the market.

But after the apple tree fell down in the storm, I didn't get to do any of that stuff anymore and I didn't get any pocket money. Dad got very grumpy and shouted at Jake all the time for no reason. And that made me mad so then I shouted at Dad. There was a lot of shouting.

3

Chance

Things went on like that for a while – lots of shouting and worrying and being grumpy. I hated it.

I missed the apple tree. After the storm, the stump of the tree was all that was left. The leaves on all the other trees started to grow again as spring came and the days grew longer. But the stump of the apple tree just stayed the same: short, stubby and dead.

Then my birthday came along, on 1 May. I love my birthday. For as long as I can remember, my birthday is always on the same day as the summer fair.

On that day, instead of selling apples at our local market, Dad and I would bring all our apples to the summer fair. It is much bigger than the local market and there are lots of people selling things. And there are also rides and games, which make it way more fun than the normal market.

So, on my birthday, I woke up and was really excited – until I remembered that we had no apples to sell so we wouldn't be going to the summer fair. Then Mum called up the stairs, "Megan, there's some post for you. It might be a birthday card."

It was a card from Granny Annie. "Dear Megan, I hope you have a lovely birthday," it said. Inside the card was a small envelope. I opened it and found a €5 note.

Then Dad said, "Well, I know we've no apples to sell this year. But since it's your birthday, do you still want to go to the summer fair?"

"Yes, please!" I shouted, feeling excited again.

A few minutes later, Mum and Dad and I were in the car, ready to go. Jake was in the garden staring at us, looking grumpy that he couldn't come too.

When we arrived at the fair, the first thing we did was go on a roller coaster. It wasn't a proper one, just a small one. I didn't really want to go on it, in case anyone from my school saw me and thought I was a baby. But, after our go was over, I realised it was actually pretty cool, even though I didn't say it out loud.

Next we got some candy floss. Well, I got candy floss and Mum and Dad got some tea. They sat down at a bench to drink it and told me not to go too far.

I was walking along, eating the candy floss and trying not to get it stuck in my hair, when I saw the wheel of fortune.

"Spin the wheel and win a prize!" shouted the man beside it. He was standing in front of a big table full of prizes. There were teddy bears and chocolates and all sorts of things. But one thing caught my eye – a teeny tiny apple tree in a pot with a ribbon around it.

And that's when I had my idea. I would spin the wheel and try to win the baby apple tree, and then Mum and Dad would be able to grow apples again. Dad would stop worrying and shouting at Jake, and Mum wouldn't be worrying, and I wouldn't be grumpy.

A big sign said: "SPIN TO WIN. €3 A GO". The €5 note that Granny Annie had sent me was in my pocket. So I handed the wheel-of-fortune man the €5 note. He gave me back a €2 coin as change.

The wheel had numbers all around it and a big arrow that moved around as the wheel turned. Each of the prizes had a number

too. So, all I had to do was spin the wheel and hope that, when it stopped, the arrow would land on the number that matched the number on the apple tree.

I waited my turn. When it was my go, I stepped up to the wheel, grabbed the handle and pulled as hard as I could. The wheel spun round and round so many times that I felt dizzy. Then it started to get slower and slower, until it stopped.

But when it stopped, the arrow didn't land on the number that matched the one on the apple tree. It didn't land on a number that matched any of the prizes. I didn't win the apple tree and I didn't even win something else. And I had spent more than half the money Granny Annie gave me.

A big fat tear rolled down my cheek. I wiped it away with my hand, but another tear raced down my cheek to take its place.

4

Ideas

The whole way home from the summer fair, the €2 coin that was left from my birthday money from Granny Annie was right in the middle of my fist, which I had deep in my pocket.

When we got home, I ran up to my room and grabbed my money box. I shook it: clink, clink, clink! I opened it and shook it again and watched as all the coins – all the money I had – came tumbling out.

There were a few shiny new coins that people had given me as presents. And then there were one or two old dirty coins that I had found down the back of the sofa. And underneath all the coins was a squished-up piece of paper. I unfolded it. It wasn't just any old piece of squished-up paper. It was a €5 note. I counted up all the money. I had €12.58.

Mum and Dad were watching television when I went downstairs. "Mum, Dad," I said.

"Mmm," they mumbled, heads still turned towards the television.

"How much would an apple tree cost?" I asked.

"Oh, you'd need a lot of money to buy a tree strong enough to grow apples," Dad said.

So that's when I had my second idea.

Remember I said I had €12.58 when I counted up all the money that I had in the world? Well, my idea was to find a way to get some more money, so that I could buy my mum and dad another apple tree.

Before the apple tree fell down, when I was trying to think of ideas, I'd go and sit under the tree with Jake beside me. "Got your thinking cap on, Meg?" Dad used to say. But this time I had to find a new thinking place, because the stump of the dead apple tree was not a very good place for ideas.

So I curled up on my bed, with Jake lying snuggled up against my tummy, and tried to think of ways to make some money. I thought and thought and thought. Paper rounds, cake sales, car washing … I had lots of ideas. But then I had my best idea. I decided I would offer to walk people's dogs in return for a little money.

That night, I used coloured pens and some paper to make some leaflets. On each sheet of paper I drew a picture of a dog, and underneath, in big letters, I wrote my phone number and the words – "Megan – the best dog walker ever".

The next day was Saturday so I had no school. I walked around my neighbourhood, pushing the leaflets through all the letter boxes. Over the next few days, I got so excited when the phone rang. I was waiting for someone to call and ask me to walk their dog.

Mrs Maguire on our street was the first person to call. "Megan," she said. "I got your lovely leaflet and thought it was such a good idea. And then just the next day I broke my leg. So now I need someone to take my dog Toby for his walk each day until I'm back on my feet."

Toby was a friendly dog. He had fluffy paws, a hairy belly and shiny brown eyes. On our first walk, we went down our street and into the park. Toby tried to chase a duck in the pond so I had to hold his lead tight to make sure he didn't run away. On the way back to Toby's house, we passed my garden. Jake looked very cranky when he saw me with a dog.

But Jake got used to it, because over the next few weeks I walked lots and lots of dogs past our house.

Summer came and went in a blur of long walks. Big dogs, small dogs, fat dogs, skinny dogs – I walked every sort of dog. Soon the leaves started to get crackly on the ground and it was time to go back to school after the holidays. And gradually my money box started to sound a little fuller when I shook it: clink, clink, clink!

5

Decisions

As the summer drew to an end and back-to-school time came closer, I decided it was time to count my money again. I took my money box off the shelf. It felt a lot heavier than before.

When I opened it up, the pile of coins that spilled out was much larger than before and there were a lot more squished-up paper notes too.

First I counted the little coins, then the big ones and then the paper notes. And then I counted it all again to make sure I was right. It all came to a grand total of €127.44! Wow! I had never seen so much money before.

Then it was time to put my plan into action. I wanted to use the money I had earned to buy a new apple tree as a surprise for Mum and Dad. They knew that I had been walking dogs all summer to make some pocket money because they couldn't afford to give me pocket money anymore. But they didn't know that I wanted to use the dog-walking money to buy them a new apple tree.

That was the surprise bit.

On the Saturday before school started again, Mum and I went shopping. While she was looking for schoolbooks and uniforms and lunch boxes, I asked her if I could have a look in some of the other shops.

"Well, don't be long," Mum said. "Be back in thirty minutes and no later."

I pretended that I was a secret agent, with just half an hour to finish my mission. I marched out the door of the shop and headed down the road, with the money I had saved to buy a new apple tree stuffed into my pocket.

On the main street in our town there are lots of shops. There's the shop with all the creamy cakes in the window. Every time I walk by it, I feel a little bit hungry. Then there's the shop that sells bicycles. That's where Mum and Dad bought me my first bicycle. Next door to the bicycle shop is a pet shop. I always stop and press my nose up against the window to look at the gold-fish in their tanks.

As I walked by the shops, I thought about all the things I could buy with the money I had saved. I could go to the cake shop and buy enough cream cakes for a whole year. Or I could buy the shiny new red bicycle in the window of the bicycle shop. Or I could buy a fluffy blanket for Jake at the pet shop.

But that day I didn't stop to buy anything else. Instead, I walked past all the other shops right to the end of the street. That's where the gardening shop is.

When I went in the door, a little bell rang above my head. Inside, it was a bit dark and smelt like flowers. It was only then I realised that I didn't really know what sort of apple tree to buy.

"Hello," said a voice. "Can I help you?" I looked around, trying to see who had spoken. Then I saw an old man standing just behind the counter.

"You're a little younger than my usual customers," he said, laughing to himself.

"I want to buy an apple tree for my mum and dad," I said.

"Mmm," he said, rubbing his chin. "I see. The apple trees are over there." He pointed towards a shelf on the other side of the shop.

There were lots of baby apple trees in rows on the shelf. They all looked the same to me, but some cost more than others. I felt confused and not very like a secret agent at all anymore. But then I had another idea – the very last bit of my plan to make everyone happy again.

6

Growing

Do you remember earlier on I told you I wanted to buy my mum and dad an apple tree, so that they didn't have to worry anymore? Well, I sort of changed my mind.

This is what happened.

I was looking at all the different types of apple trees and getting confused. The man in the shop came over and asked if he could help. I tried to explain why I wanted an apple tree and suddenly I was blurting out the whole story. I told him about the storm and the apple tree falling down, and not having any apples to sell at the market anymore, and my parents worrying and me being grumpy.

"Do your parents grow anything else, or just apples?" asked the man from the gardening shop.

"No, just apples," I said. And that's when I changed my mind just a bit about buying an apple tree.

You see, I still bought a tiny apple tree. But I also bought other things with the money I had left over. I bought a small raspberry bush, a strawberry plant and some seeds to grow vegetables.

I ran all the way back through the town to meet my mum. I was late and she was wondering where I had been.

"And what have you been buying, Megan?" she asked, sighing when she saw all my bags from the gardening shop.

In the car on the way home, I told her about my secret plan to make everyone happy again.

"That's very thoughtful, Megan," she said, smiling.

When we got home, Dad was sitting on the garden bench, reading his newspaper.

"Dad, I have a surprise for you," I said. I was talking really fast because I was so excited. "I bought a new apple tree and seeds and lots of stuff, and we can grow apples again and go to the market on Saturdays and not have to worry anymore. And no more shouting."

"Slow down a bit," Dad said. "Go back to the beginning and explain it all to me again."

So I told him that I used my dog-walking money to buy seeds and plants and a new tree. "That's a great surprise, Meg," he said. "I'm very proud of you."

That afternoon Dad and I got out our spades and dug the ground. First we planted the new apple tree. It's really small for now, but one day I hope it will be as tall as our old apple tree.

Next we planted the raspberry bush and the strawberry plant. Then we planted rows and rows of lettuce and tomato seeds.

So that's my story. The apple tree fell down. And everyone worried. And then I had a plan to make everything okay, a bit like a secret mission. And then we planted lots of new stuff.

But wait, before you go, I suppose I should tell you one last little bit, to finish my story off.

It's ages since the apple tree blew down in the storm. And now Dad and I are going to the market every Saturday again. We sell apples and berries and lettuce and tomatoes, not just apples like before. And Mum still makes apple cake from the bumpy apples, but now she uses the berries to make jam too.

The new apple tree is not very tall yet, so Jake has found a new place to escape the sun. Now he sits under the raspberry bush.

And me? Well, I don't have a huge, twisty apple tree in my garden anymore. But every time I look out my window, I see the new apple tree growing taller and taller.

II

A Guide for Grown-Ups

1

Crash – A Guide for Grown-Ups

Key learning point: unexpected things happen

Summary

What happened in this chapter?

Readers met Megan and heard about her family, learning that her parents had an apple tree and grew apples, which her dad then sold at the local market to gain a source of income for the family. However, disaster struck when the apple tree fell down during a storm.

Some questions for your child:

1. What did Megan think the leaves on the apple tree were when she was little?
    Megan's dad used to joke that the apple tree was his "money tree". So Megan thought the leaves on the apple tree were €10 notes.

Next, narrow the list to unexpected financial events. This could include winning the lottery, inheriting some money or losing your job.

Activities

Learn some new words with Megan...

1. **Income** – the money people earn for the work they do.
   – *Explain to your child that people also use the words wages and salary to refer to income.*
2. **Market** – a place where people sell things.
3. **Job** – what people do to earn money.

Help Megan with a mission...

Megan wants to find out how much money her family would earn if they sold an apple. Can you help her to find out?

To complete this mission:

Take your child along to the supermarket on your next visit. Together, find some apples and check the price. Talk about the work that goes into producing each apple and the money earned from selling each apple, and use this to get your child thinking about the value of money.

Play one of Megan's games...

Category – logic

Can you guess how much things cost? Megan wants your help to figure out the price of some things.

Setting up the game – a guide for grown-ups

Take an assortment of items from around the house and line them all up on the table. Write down a price for each item on a piece of paper, according to what you imagine they would cost. Fold up the piece of paper and place it under the corresponding item. Get your child to guess what price each item is and to order the items from cheapest to dearest. Then reveal the actual prices. This exercise will help your child to appreciate the relative value of things.

2

Changes – A Guide for Grown-Ups

Key learning point: events have consequences

Summary

What happened in this chapter?

Megan told us about the time before the storm and what her family would do with the apples. They would pick them and bring them to the market each Saturday. If any of the apples were 'bumpy', Megan's mum made them into an apple cake. When the weather was good, Megan and her cat Jake would sit in the shade of the apple tree. And, at Halloween, they had toffee apples. But when the apple tree fell down in the storm, everything changed. Megan's parents were worried all the time about not having enough money. And Megan no longer got her pocket money every Saturday.

Some questions for your child...

1. Why did Megan's family not have any apples to sell anymore?
   They had no more apples to sell because the apple tree fell down during the storm.
   – *Use this question to talk about the chapter's key learning point – events, that you can't predict or prevent, have consequences.*

2. What did her mum do with the bumpy apples?
   If the apples were bumpy and not good enough to sell, Megan's mum made them into apple cake.
   – *Use this question to introduce the idea of using resources carefully.*

3. Why were her parents worried?
   Megan's parents were worried because they had lost their source of income and did not know how they would pay their bills.
   – *Use this question to talk about the reasons why people need money.*

4. Why was Megan frustrated?
   She was frustrated because she did not like being treated like a baby. She understood that her parents were worried about money and did not want them to pretend that everything was fine.
   – *Use this question to talk about how a family could cope if they had less money.*

5. Why do you think Megan didn't get pocket money
    anymore?
    Megan used to get her pocket money on Saturdays
    after she had helped her dad to sell the apples at
    the market. After the apple tree fell down, her par-
    ents weren't able to afford to give her pocket money
    anymore.
    – *Use this question to talk about getting pocket
    money and where the money comes from.*

Explanation

So, what's the point?

After reading this chapter and discussing the questions, your child will have thought about how an
unexpected event can change daily life. To put this in
financial terms, families can find it hard to cope when
they have less money.

How do I explain this concept to my child?

First, ask your child to think about why we need to
earn money. Make a list of all the things that families
have to pay for, such as food, clothes, heating, television channels and birthday presents.

   Help your child to understand that some things are
necessities, while others are luxuries. Divide your list
of expenses into needs and wants, and help your child
to understand the difference.

   Discuss with your child the reasons why families
might have less money. Next, explain that families

would have to prioritise their spending if their budget shrinks.

Identifying similar situations...

In the story, Megan's family had less money because their income was reduced unexpectedly. Event: the tree fell down. Consequence: a lower income for the family.

With your child, make a list of other actions and events that would have financial consequences. For example, if a family decide to buy a bigger car, they will have to pay more money for it. Or if a parent gets a new job, he or she might earn a higher salary.

Activities

Learn some new words with Megan...

1. **Bills** – the money you have to pay for services like water, heating and electricity.
2. **Loan** – money that you borrow and repay with interest to the bank.
3. **Debt** – the amount of money that you owe people.

Help Megan with a mission...

Megan wants to understand household bills and how much a family spends on things. Can you help her?

To complete this mission:

With your child, take a look at your most recent electricity bill. Ask your child to make a list of the various charges applied. This could include a standing charge, monthly charges and so on. Now look back at some previous bills. Is the amount of money spent on electricity each month different? Discuss why the amount is higher for some months than for others and ask your child to explain some possible reasons for this fluctuation. For example, cold weather means having the heat on more, which results in a higher bill.

Play one of Megan's games...

Category – active
Can you complete an obstacle course? If you are fast, Megan has a reward for you.

Setting up the game – a guide for grown-ups

Make an obstacle course in your garden (or inside if you prefer) for your child. This can involve whatever activities you like, such as skipping, jumping jacks and so on. Give your child a target time and then time your child completing the course. For every second under the target time they are, give them an imaginary budget of €1.

Now assign a value to household chores and activities, e.g. making bed = €0.50, an extra 30 minutes watching television = €1.50. Let your child spend his or her notional budget accumulated from the earlier activity. This game will show your child that different outcomes have different results, and will also help him or her to appreciate the value of money.

3

Chance – A Guide for Grown-Ups

> **Key learning point: risks don't always pay off**

Summary

What happened in this chapter?

The chapter began with Megan telling readers that she missed the apple tree and was sick of everyone in her house worrying and being grumpy. Things started to look up when her birthday came around and her Granny Annie sent her €5 as a present. Megan and her parents visited the annual summer fair as a treat. Even though they had no apples to sell this year, they still enjoyed the day. They went on a roller coaster and Megan had some candy floss. Then Megan decided to spend some of her birthday money on the wheel of fortune in a bid to win a baby apple tree. However, she didn't win a prize and was upset that she had wasted some of her birthday money.

Some questions for your child...

1. Why did Megan and her dad normally go to the summer fair?
    The summer fair was on Megan's birthday, 1 May. On that day each year, Megan and her dad went to the summer fair to sell apples, instead of selling them at their local market.
    – Use this question to talk about the benefits of a bigger market, i.e. potential to sell more apples and make more money.

2. Would Megan and her family have spent much money on their outing?
    The family would have had to pay for petrol for their car to get there. Also, they would have had to pay to go on the roller coaster and to buy candy floss and tea.
    – Use this question to help your child to understand the costs involved in family outings.

3. How did Megan choose to spend the money her Granny Annie sent her?
    Megan spent €3 of the €5 on the wheel of fortune and brought her €2 change home.
    – Use this question to discuss the choices we face when spending money.

4. Did Megan have a good chance of winning the prize?

The wheel of fortune was based on luck alone, so there was no way for Megan to predict if she would win or not.
– Use this question to introduce your child to the concept of risk in financial decisions.

5. Would you have spun the wheel?
    There is no right or wrong answer to this question. Instead, the answer depends on a personal appetite for risk.
    – Use this question to get your child thinking about how people are prepared to take different levels of risk.

Explanation

So, what's the point?

After reading this chapter and discussing the questions, your child will have thought about the chances we take from time to time. In financial terms, some investments pay off and others don't.

How do I explain this concept to my child?

First, ask your child to talk to you about the choice that Megan made when she played the wheel-of-fortune game. Discuss the other possible outcomes. Megan could have decided not to play the game, taken no risk and kept all the money her Granny Annie sent her for her birthday. Or taking a risk could have paid off, if she had won the apple tree.

Ask your child to think about what he or she would have done in the same scenario and to make a list of the advantages and disadvantages of each option.

Identifying similar situations...

Think of some other situations where people take financial risks. Try to get your child to weigh up the pros and cons of each situation.

Some examples include betting on a horse in a race, buying a lottery ticket or buying shares in a new company. For the latter example, explain to your child that investing in a company means you own a tiny bit of it. So, if the company does well and makes lots of money, you will benefit. But, likewise, if the company does not do well, you could end up with nothing.

Activities

Learn some new words with Megan...

1. **Share** – the portion of a company you own when you invest in it.
2. **Investing** – like saving, but you want to get a better return on your money.
3. **Risk** – the possibility that an outcome can be good or bad, due to the unexpected nature of things.

Help Megan with a mission...

Sometimes Megan likes to imagine what she'd do if she had €5 to spend on herself. She's curious about what others would spend €5 on and has asked her friends

Aisling and Ciara what they would do. Imagine she asks you. How would you reply?

To complete this mission:

This exercise will introduce your child to a number of ideas. First, it will help your child to draw up a wish list of all the things he or she might like to buy. He or she can then attempt to guess the cost of each item on the wish list. Help your child to prioritise the items they would like to buy first.

Play one of Megan's games...

Category – logic
Can you tell what the future holds? Megan wants you to roll the dice to see what's in store.

Setting up the game – a guide for grown-ups

Make a list of funny activities, such as wearing a silly hat, jumping on one leg or pretending to be a monkey. Number the activities from one to twelve. Next, take two dice and, with your child, take it in turns to roll the two dice together. Add up your score and find the corresponding activity on the list. For example, if you roll a 2 on one dice and a 5 on the other, you have to do the seventh activity on the list. This game will help your child to understand that certain things are hard to predict, and that we have to be prepared for a range of different outcomes. It will also give them a chance to practise their counting and addition skills.

4

Ideas – A Guide for Grown-Ups

Key learning point: saving is gradual, with no quick fix

Summary

What happened in this chapter?

This chapter began with Megan counting all the money she had in her money box, following her disappointment at the summer fair in the previous chapter. After missing out on winning an apple tree with the wheel-of-fortune game, she asked her parents how much it would cost to buy a new apple tree. She realised that she couldn't rely on luck and instead tried to think of other ways to fund the purchase of a new apple tree. Megan spent her summer walking dogs for her neighbours, and gradually saved the money she needed to buy a new tree.

Some questions for your child...

1. How much money did Megan have at the beginning and where did she keep it?

    Megan had €12.58 in her money box. Her money was a mixture of small coins, big coins and paper notes.

    – *Use this question to talk about saving money in a money box or in a savings account.*

2. Why did she want to earn more money?

    Megan wanted more money so that she could buy her parents a new apple tree and restore their source of income. She hoped her plan would mean her family would not have to worry so much.

    – *Use this question to talk about setting goals when saving.*

3. What did Megan consider doing to earn more money?

    When Megan decided that she needed more money, she curled up on her bed with Jake the cat to think of ways to earn money. She thought about getting a job delivering papers, making cakes and selling them, or washing cars. In the end, she decided to walk dogs for people in return for payment.

    – *Use this question to reinforce the earlier lesson about how people earn money (Chapter 1, Part II).*

4. What would you have done to earn more money?

This is a more subjective question and allows your child to express his or her own view. Perhaps, when discussing this question and answer, adults and children could consider the pros and cons of each potential job.

– Use this question to talk about how your child would like to earn money when they are older.

5. Did Megan's plan take long to put into action?
Towards the end of this chapter, Megan told readers, "Summer came and went in a blur of long walks." She put a lot of time into making her plan to earn money a success, walking all sorts of dogs during her summer holidays.

– Use this question to explain this chapter's key learning point – saving is gradual process, with no quick fix.

Explanation

So, what's the point?

After reading this chapter and discussing the questions, your child will have thought about the time it takes to make a plan a reality. To put this in financial terms, building up enough money to meet financial goals and objectives takes time.

How do I explain this concept to my child?

Together with your child, discuss the steps involved in building a house. First, a plan is drawn up; next, the foundations are dug; then blocks are laid; and finally a roof goes on top. Only when this basic work is done can you start to decorate inside the house and fill it with furniture. Your child should recognise that this is a gradual process, and one that takes time to complete.

Draw a comparison between building a house and saving money. When people save, they typically have a goal in mind, such as buying a house, going on holidays or paying off a large bill. This is just like the plan for building a house.

Laying the groundwork and starting a savings habit is just like building the foundations of a house. Without strong foundations, the house won't survive. Equally, without a consistent, methodical approach, it will be hard to meet savings targets.

With a house, it is vital to sort out all the basics before you think about décor and so on. Equally, when people save, they tend to prioritise their needs ahead of their wants. For example – you have a broken window, but you also want to buy new shoes. If you plan to use your savings to pay for these items, it makes sense to prioritise the repair of the broken window. Explain to your child that some of the things we spend money on are necessities, while other things are not essential.

Identifying similar situations...

With your child, draw up a list of situations when people make plans. This could include planning a birthday party, planning how to get somewhere using a map or planning a holiday.

Discuss the steps involved in each plan. Talk about how somebody could put the plan into action and how long this would take.

For example, to plan a birthday party you would start by deciding what day you want to hold the party. Next, you'd decide who you wanted to come. Then you'd send invitations and await responses. Finally, you'd prepare food for your guests and choose the music to play at the party. However, remember that things may change and some people might cancel at the last minute.

Explain to your child that making a financial plan is much the same. It's simply a case of deciding your objective and following the necessary steps to achieve it. However, as we saw in Chapter 1 (Part I and Part II), unexpected things can happen and could make it harder to achieve your goal.

Activities

Learn some new words with Megan...

1. **Deposit** – putting your money in the bank.
2. **Withdraw** – taking your money out of the bank.
3. **Interest** – the payment you receive from the bank for letting them mind your money.

Help Megan with a mission...

Megan wants to start saving her money in the bank. Can you tell her how to do it?

To complete this mission:

Teach your child about how to start saving. The next time you go to the bank, bring your child along. Together, take a look at a lodgement slip and try to fill it in. Perhaps you could open a special young saver account for your child and help him or her to begin to develop a savings habit.

Play one of Megan's games...

Category – creative
Do you have somewhere special to keep your money? Megan wants you to decorate a money box.

Setting up the game – a guide for grown-ups

Saving can be fun and it is important that your child does not view saving as something dull. One way of making saving interesting is to make the process as entertaining as possible for your child. Instead of just having a boring money box on the shelf, help your child to make a more appealing money box. Take an old glass jar or a tub, or any other container from around the house. This is your child's new money box. Help him or her to make it colourful and friendly looking. Decorate it using paint, markers or whatever else comes to hand. This activity will teach your child about saving and having a place to put their money.

5

Decisions – A Guide for Grown-Ups

Key learning point: opportunity costs exist when you make a purchase

Summary

What happened in this chapter?

Megan once again counted all the money in her money box. This time, after a summer spent walking dogs, she had a lot more money than before. Before she returned to school after the holidays, she decided to complete the final part of her plan. She went shopping with her mum, intending to slip away for a few minutes to buy her parents a new apple tree. However, on her way to the gardening shop, Megan walked past all the other shops and learned that buying one item meant sacrificing another.

Some questions for your child...

1. How much money was in Megan's money box?
    How much more was there than the last time she
    counted her money?
    Megan had €127.44 in her money box, compared
    with €12.58 when she counted her money the last
    time. This meant she had €114.86 more than before.
    *– Use this question to familiarise your child with
    adding and subtracting sums of money, calculating
    change and so on.*

2. How did Megan get the extra money?
    Megan earned the extra money by walking dogs for
    people in return for a little money.
    *– Use this question to reinforce the earlier learning
    point about the work that people do to earn money
    (Chapter 1, Part II).*

3. What else could Megan have bought with the
    money she had?
    As Megan walked down the road to the gardening
    shop, she thought about the other things she could
    buy with the money she had earned and saved. She
    thought that she could go to the cake shop and buy
    enough cream cakes for a whole year or buy the
    shiny new red bicycle in the window of the bicycle
    shop. Another option was to buy a fluffy blanket for
    her cat Jake at the pet shop.

– Use this question to talk about the choices we face when spending money.

4. What would you have bought with the money?
This is another subjective question, and allows your child to consider the choices they would make if they were in Megan's position.
– Use this question to get your child thinking about their own spending priorities.

5. Why was Megan confused at the end of this chapter?
Megan was confused because she did not know which apple tree to buy for her parents. She was a little overwhelmed by the number of different apple trees on sale in the shop, and was not sure which one would represent the best purchase for her.
– Use this question to talk about getting the best possible value for money when making a purchase.

Explanation

So, what's the point?

After reading this chapter and discussing the questions, your child will have thought about the choices we face every day. To put this in financial terms, each purchase we make generally means foregoing another purchase.

How do I explain this concept to my child?

The key message to get across to your child from this chapter is that resources are finite. To begin, you could take some Lego or building blocks and ask your child to use the blocks to make two houses.

If your child uses too many blocks to build the first house, there will be none left over for the second one. Talk to your child about dividing the available bricks between the two houses, and explain why you are splitting the resources equally. Explain to your child that people face similar decisions with money. Using all your money to buy one item means there is no money left for other purchases.

Identifying similar situations...

Ask your child to think of times when they faced a choice. For example, he or she may have wanted to go to a birthday party, but the event could have clashed with a regular activity, such as swimming or dancing. He or she may have wanted to do both, but, given that time was limited, a choice had to be made.

Explain to your child that when we spend money we face a similar decision. In this case it is money, not time, that is limited. So we must choose the items we want to buy and recognise that we are unable to buy the other items due to our limited resources.

Activities

Learn some new words with Megan...

1. **Asset** – something we own, such as money, a house or a car.
2. **Budget** – a financial plan.
3. **Expense** – something we have to pay for.

Help Megan with a mission...

Megan has saved some money and wants to know what to spend it on. Can you help her to decide?

To complete this mission:

This activity will help your child to understand that money has different purposes. Some of our money is needed to pay for essentials, while some of it can fund more fun expenses. The remainder should be kept as a rainy day fund to provide for unexpected events. Get your child to take three identical jars or tubs. Label them as "Need", "Want" and "Maybe", to reflect the three different uses for money. When your child receives a gift of money or pocket money, encourage them to split the money equally between the three jars. If they choose to buy something, discuss which type of spending it is and which jar they should take the money from. For example, a new toy is not a necessity and is a discretionary purchase, meaning that the money to buy it comes from the "Want" jar. And what if something unexpected happens? Suppose your child loses their swimming goggles and wants to buy new ones? This could be funded from the "Maybe" jar.

Play one of Megan's games...

Category – creative

Can you draw? Megan wants you to draw a picture of her and her cat Jake.

Setting up the game – a guide for grown-ups

Ask your child to draw three pictures of Megan and her cat Jake. For the first picture, give your child just a blank piece of paper and a pencil. For the second picture, give your child some coloured pencils or crayons too. And for the third picture, give your child some glue and glitter, ribbon or pieces of coloured tissue paper to stick to the page. Each of the three pictures will be very different. This game will help to explain to your child that varying levels of resources result in different outcomes.

6

Growing – A Guide for Grown-Ups

> **Key learning point: diversifying minimises risk**

Summary

What happened in this chapter?

Megan changed her mind a bit and adapted her plan slightly. Instead of buying just a new apple tree, she used the money she had saved to buy a variety of new plants. She told her parents about her secret plan and was delighted that she had made everyone happy again. She planted the new tree and also fruit bushes and vegetables, meaning her family never had to rely on just one tree again.

Some questions for your child...

1. How did Megan's plan change?
   Initially, she had intended to buy a new apple tree for her parents. However, she changed her mind

and used the money she had saved to buy a variety of new plants.
– Use this question to introduce the idea of not putting all your eggs in one basket.

2. Apart from an apple tree, what did Megan buy?
She bought a small raspberry bush, a strawberry plant and some seeds to grow vegetables.
– Use this question to talk about how Megan has reduced the risk of future income shocks and made her family less reliant on the apple tree.

3. What does her family sell now?
Megan's family now sell apples, berries, lettuce and tomatoes at the market, not just apples like before. Her mum still makes apple cake from the bumpy apples, but now she uses the berries to make jam too.
– Use this question to discuss how Megan's family have developed their business and now have more income sources.

4. What would happen if the new apple tree was blown down in a storm?
Megan's family do not rely on the apple tree as much as they used to. So, if another storm hit and the new apple tree fell down, their income would fall a little bit. However, they would still have income from other sources.

– Use this question to talk about how financial risk can be reduced.

5. Where does Megan's cat Jake go to escape the sun? Jake used to sleep in the shade under the old apple tree, but now he sits under the raspberry bush.
– Use this question to discuss how people can adapt to the new circumstances they face as a result of financial changes.

Explanation

So, what's the point?

After reading this chapter and discussing the questions, your child will have thought about keeping their options open when making a decision. To put this in financial terms, spreading your investments across a variety of asset classes means you reduce the level of risk that you face.

How do I explain this concept to my child?

To explain the concept of diversifying risk to your child, perhaps it would be useful to draw a comparison between this and sport.

Ask your child to think about the risks involved in a penalty shoot-out in an important football match. Imagine the game will be decided on a "best of three" basis, with each team taking three shots at goal.

The first team decides to let three different strikers take a shot at goal, while the second team chooses just one player to take all three kicks.

Explain to your child that the first team is spreading its risk in a bid to maximise its chances of winning the match. This is the same rationale that investors use when they divide their money among different investments in the hope that they will generate a bigger return than if they put all their money into one type of investment.

Identifying similar situations...

Talk to your child about things that people do to reduce risk. This could include taking vitamins regularly to make sure they don't get sick, wearing a seat-belt when travelling by car or wearing a bicycle helmet when cycling.

Explain to your child that people do these things to protect themselves in situations where something bad could happen. Similarly, investors take precautions to reduce their chances of losing money.

Activities

Learn some new words with Megan ...

1. **Diversify** – dividing your money between different types of investment to make it less risky.
2. **Investor** – a person who invests money.
3. **Shareholder** – a person who owns a bit of a company.

Help Megan with a mission...

Megan wants to know more about the world of business and finance. Can you help her?

To complete this mission:

With your child, take a look at the business section of a newspaper or a news website. Pick a simple story and try to explain it to your child in easy-to-follow terms. For example, if a large quoted company has announced results, explain to your child why all the people who own shares will be interested to see how the company is doing. Or, if a bank has increased mortgage interest rates, explain to your child that people who own houses will now have to pay more money to the bank. The objective is not to overwhelm your child, but merely to make him or her more familiar with the language of money.

Play one of Megan's games...

Category – active
Can you grow things? Megan wants your help to plant some seeds.

Setting up the game – a guide for grown-ups

With your child, buy some inexpensive seeds or save the seeds from inside used fruit or vegetables. Plant the seeds in two different pots and place one indoors and the other outdoors. Over the coming weeks, water the pot that is inside and tend to it carefully. Meanwhile ignore the pot of seeds outside. Track the progress of each set of seeds. Which pot shows signs of growth first? By ignoring the seeds in the second pot, you are taking a risk that they will not grow. But if they do grow, you will have a new plant with very little effort. Use this activity to teach your child that different outcomes and different levels of risk are likely with investments.